ICE AGE 4
CONTINENTAL DRIFT

Popcorn
ELT
Readers

Meet ... everyone in ICE AGE 4
CONTINENTAL DRIFT

I'm Sid. I'm a sloth. I'm always happy.

I'm Manny. I'm a mammoth.

I'm Ellie.

I'm Peaches. Manny is my dad and Ellie is my mum.

I'm Diego. I'm a sabre-toothed tiger.

I'm Captain Gutt. We're pirates.

I'm Shira. I'm a sabre-toothed tiger too.

Before you read ...
What do you think?
Are the pirates good or bad?

New Words

What do these new words mean? Ask your teacher or use your dictionary.

family

This is a **family**.

crack

There is a **crack** in the house.
The house is **cracking**.

fight

The boys are **fighting**.

escape

The man is **escaping**.

help

The boy is **helping** his mother.

iceberg

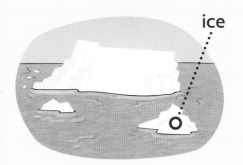

ice

The **iceberg** is in the sea.

prisoner

The man is a **prisoner**.

jump

The lion is **jumping**.

ship

The **ship** is on the sea.

kill

Cats **kill** small animals.

'Let us go!'

Let us go!

What does *Continental Drift* mean? Ask your teacher.

CHAPTER ONE
A big crack

One day Manny is with his family and friends.

'Hi, Sid. Hi, Diego,' he says.

'Hi, Manny,' says Sid. 'How are … ?'

But then there is a big crack!

'What's that?' asks Sid.

Everyone listens.

'Dad!' shouts Peaches. 'The ice is cracking!'

'Quick! Run away!' shouts Manny.

The ice cracks in front of Manny and Sid.

Diego jumps to help his friends.
Suddenly they are on a big iceberg.
'We can't stop!' says Diego. 'The
iceberg is going out to the sea.'
'Ellie! Peaches!' shouts Manny.

It's very windy and it starts to rain. Soon it is night and the sea is dark. The iceberg goes up and down.

'We're far from home now,' says Manny.

'Look!' says Diego. 'What's that?'
They see a big ice ship.
There are animals on the ship.

CHAPTER TWO
The pirate ship

'Hello,' says a big monkey on the ship. 'I'm Captain Gutt. I'm your friend. Come and eat something.'

'Oh thank you. I'm hungry,' says Sid.

Diego sees another tiger on the ship.
'Who are you?' he asks.
'My name's Shira,' says the tiger.
'Shira's a nice name,' thinks Diego.

'We're pirates,' says Captain Gutt.

'Oh no!' says Sid.

'Are you a pirate too, Shira?' asks Diego.

'Yes, she is. We're all pirates and you are my prisoners,' laughs Captain Gutt.

Diego, Manny and Sid fight the pirates but they can't escape.

'Help!' says Sid. 'Let us go!'

The pirates are very happy. Captain Gutt sings and dances.

'Come and be pirates with us,' he says to Manny.

'No,' says Manny. 'I'm going home to my family.'

'You're not going home,' answers Captain Gutt.

'Let's kill the sloth first,' he says to his pirates.

'Stop!' says Shira. 'Don't kill him.'

Diego and Manny escape and they help Sid.

'Quick! Let's jump onto that iceberg!' shouts Diego.

'Captain Gutt is a bad monkey,' thinks Shira. Then she jumps too.

Diego is angry with Shira.

'Go away! You're a pirate,' he says.

'No,' answers Shira. 'I'm not a pirate now.
I can help you. We can escape.'

'Let's go!' says Manny. 'Let's go home.'
But the pirate ship is not far behind.
Captain Gutt is coming!

CHAPTER THREE
Going home

The pirates are looking for Manny and his friends.

'Where are they?' asks Captain Gutt. 'They can't escape. I want my prisoners.

Manny and his friends are on the sea for many days. Then they see something.

'Look, we're home!' says Manny. Then Diego sees the pirates.

'Oh no! Captain Gutt is here too,' he says.

'Hello again, Manny,' says Captain Gutt. He is very angry. 'Look! I have some new prisoners. They are your family.'

'Help! Let us go!' says Peaches.

'Your dad can't help you now!' laughs Captain Gutt.

'We can fight the pirates,' says Diego to Manny. Shira looks at Diego.

'Yes,' says Shira. 'I can fight too.'

Manny and his friends fight the pirates.
'Now I'm very angry!' says Manny.
He runs at Captain Gutt.
'Let my family go!' shouts Manny.
'I can't fight an angry mammoth,' says
Captain Gutt and he runs away.

'Ellie! Peaches!' says Manny. 'Are you OK?'

'Yes,' says Ellie. 'Thank you. You're a good dad.'

'And you're a good friend,' says Sid.

'Thank you for your help, Shira,' says Diego. 'You're a good friend too.'

THE END

Real World

The Continents

In *Ice Age 4*, the continents move.
Let's read about continents.

200 million years ago

There is one big continent.

Today

There are seven continents:
North America, South
America, Africa, Australia,
Europe, Asia and Antarctica.

Moving slowly

The continents are on plates.
These plates move and the
continents move with them. The
name for this is continental drift.

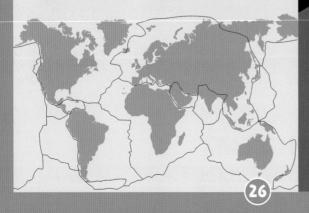

DID YOU KNOW ...?

The continents are
moving today. America
is moving away from
Europe about
2.5 centimetres a year.

Mountains

The moving plates make mountains very slowly. The Himalayan Mountains are growing about 6 centimetres a year. Are there mountains in your country?

Earthquakes

When the plates move suddenly they sometimes make earthquakes. Roads and houses can crack. Are there earthquakes in your country?

Volcanoes

There are sometimes volcanoes on the cracks next to two plates.

★ **Which continent do you live on?** ★

volcano ·········o

What do these words mean? Find out.

move   plate   mountain   grow   earthquake

After you read

1 Put the sentences in order. Write 1-7.

a) The pirates run away. ☐

b) Manny and his friends are prisoners on the pirate ship. ☐

c) The ice cracks. 1

d) Manny and his friends see a big ice ship. ☐

e) Manny and his friends are on an iceberg. ☐

f) Manny and his friends escape with Shira. ☐

g) Peaches and Ellie are prisoners. ☐

2 Who says this? Read and match.

a) 'The ice is cracking!'

b) 'We can't stop!'

c) 'Quick! Run away!'

d) 'You're not going home.'

e) 'Oh thank you. I'm hungry.'

f) 'I can fight too.'

i) Manny

ii) Captain Gutt

iii) Sid

iv) Shira

v) Diego

vi) Peaches

Where's the popcorn?
Look in your book.
Can you find it?

Puzzle time!

1 Put the icebergs in order. Write the word.

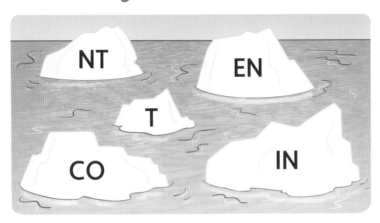

NT

EN

T

CO

IN

_ _ _ _ _ _ _ _ _ _

2 Look and write the words.

_ _ _ _ _ _ _

_ _ _ _ _ _ _

_ _ _ _ _ _ _

_ _ _ _

3 Find and circle five verbs from the story.

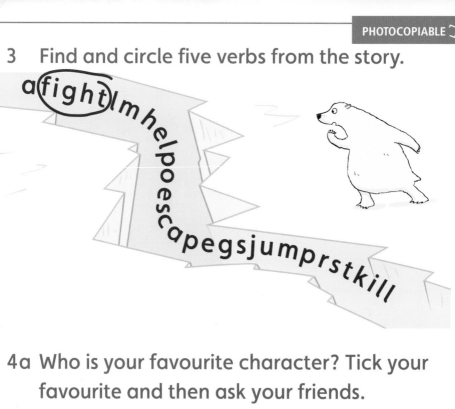

a fight lm help o escape gs jump rst kill

4a Who is your favourite character? Tick your favourite and then ask your friends.

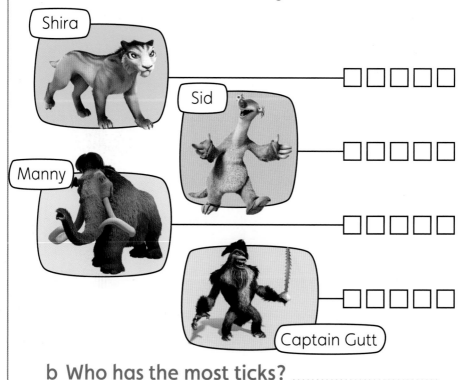

Shira ☐☐☐☐☐

Sid ☐☐☐☐☐

Manny ☐☐☐☐☐

Captain Gutt ☐☐☐☐☐

b Who has the most ticks? ....

Imagine...

1 Work in groups of four. Act out the scene.

Captain Gutt: Hello, I'm Captain Gutt. I am your friend. Come and eat something.

Sid: Oh thank you. I'm hungry.

Diego: Who are you?

Shira: My name's Shira.

Diego: Shira's a nice name.

Captain Gutt: We're pirates.

Sid: Oh no!

Diego: Are you a pirate too, Shira?

Captain Gutt: Yes, she is. We're all pirates and you are my prisoners.

Sid: Help! Let us go!

Chant

1 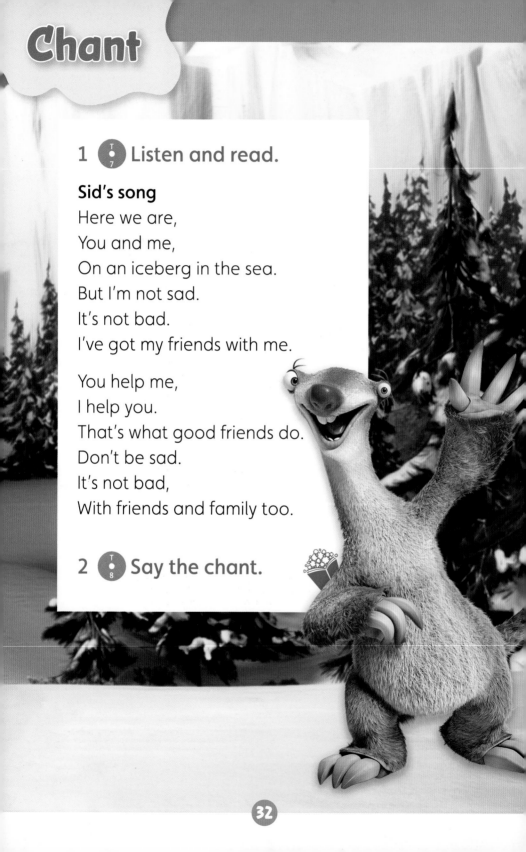 **Listen and read.**

Sid's song
Here we are,
You and me,
On an iceberg in the sea.
But I'm not sad.
It's not bad.
I've got my friends with me.

You help me,
I help you.
That's what good friends do.
Don't be sad.
It's not bad,
With friends and family too.

2 **Say the chant.**